Richard Musman

Escape in New York

DELTA Publishing

You can listen to *Escape in New York* using the free DELTA Augmented app – you'll also find fun interactive activities!

Download the free DELTA Augmented app onto your device	Start picture recognition and scan the **contents pages**	Download files and use them now or save them for later

Apple and the Apple logo are trademarks of Apple Inc., registered in the US and other countries. App Store is a service mark of Apple Inc. | Google Play and the Google Play logo are trademarks of Google Inc.

Photos: 4 Shutterstock (VOOK), New York; 5 Shutterstock (Marko Vesel), New York; 7 Shutterstock (Jam Norasett), New York; 16 Shutterstock (Victor Moussa), New York; 20 Shutterstock (Ryan DeBerardinis), New York; 25 Shutterstock (Joshua Haviv), New York; 27 Shutterstock (J2R), New York; 32 Shutterstock (Nick Starichenko), New York; 39 Shutterstock (Javen), New York; 46 Shutterstock (Sean Pavone), New York; 52 Shutterstock (Nestor Noci), New York; 57 Shutterstock (Massimo Salesi), New York; 65 Shutterstock (Photo Spirit), New York; 72 Shutterstock (spyarm), New York; 82 Shutterstock (Luca_ Luppi), New York; 90 Shutterstock (Martial Red), New York

1st edition 1 ⁵ ⁴ ³ ² ¹ | 2023 22 21 20 19

Delta Publishing, 2019
www.deltapublishing.co.uk
© Ernst Klett Sprachen GmbH, Rotebühlstraße 77, 70178 Stuttgart, 2018

Authors: Text: Richard Musman
                  Annotations and activities: Catherine Zgouras
Cover and layout: Andreas Drabarek, Stuttgart, Germany
Illustrations: Grit Döhnel
Maps: G. Wustmann, Mötzingen, Germany
Design: Datagroup Int, Timisoara, Romania
Cover picture: iStockophoto, Calgary, Alberta
Printing and binding: Salzland Druck, Staßfurt, Germany

ISBN 978-3-12-501112-0

Contents

Abbreviations

AE	American English
BE	British English
sb	somebody
sth	something
opp	opposite

Before you start

New York is famous for so many reasons. What do you know about New York in connection with the words below?

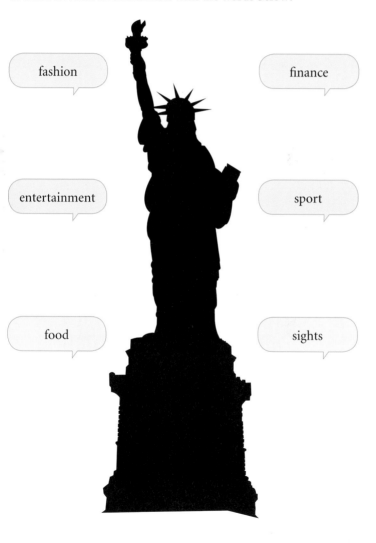

fashion

finance

entertainment

sport

food

sights

1 A meeting at Niagara Falls

The coffee shop was empty. Kevin pushed the cup away from
him and placed his arms on the counter. He had just left school
and was off to New York in a week's time to be a tourist guide.
He had spent a year in New York when he was fifteen and knew
the city well. His Aunt Bella, who he was going to stay with, had
found him the job, and he had had no difficulty in getting a work
permit.

A boy and a girl came into the coffee shop. "Hi, Kev!" "Hi, Di!
Hi, Doug!" Everyone liked Kevin, but his friends knew that there
were moments when he wanted to be left alone. Doug and Di
passed him by and sat down at a table near the window. Kevin
was thinking of his mother. She was going to marry a Toronto
businessman he did not like. He had told his mother exactly what

19 **coffee shop** place where you can get coffee and a quick, simple meal – 20 **counter**
you can sit at the counter and drink your coffee – 21 **to be off to** to be going to –
21 **tourist guide** sb who shows visitors around and tells them about the history – 24 **work
permit** a document which says that you can work – 29 **to pass sb by** to walk past sb

7

he thought of his future stepfather. She had replied that it was none of his business. "OK, Mom! Marry him, but don't expect me to come and live with you." "Do what you like, Kev," she had said. He did not want to live alone in the house in Niagara Falls, so he had written to his Aunt Bella. He and Aunt Bella were great friends.

The thunder of the waterfall reminded him that the only thing that was interesting in Niagara Falls, Canada, was the Falls! There was nothing to keep him at home. It was at that moment that he saw opposite him, on the other side of the counter, a girl he had never seen before. She had a heart-shaped face and a large mouth. Her hair was very dark and fell below her ears. Her bangs hung halfway down her forehead.

"Want anything else, Kev?" asked Betty, the girl behind the counter. He and Betty had been at school together. She was pretty, but she had nothing interesting to talk about. He shook his head and looked again at the girl across the counter. Her eyes, which were a bright blue, were full of anxiety, and she kept looking towards the door as if she was expecting an unwelcome visitor.

"Hi!" he said, walking round the counter and sitting down beside her.

The girl looked at him with surprise. "Hi!" she said.

"Let me get you a coffee," he said, "or do you want something to eat?"

She smiled. "I don't know why you are doing this. You don't know me."

"Well, I'll be honest with you. You look as though you're in trouble. I wondered if perhaps I could help you."

---

1 **stepfather** man married to your mother (not your father) – 2 **it was none of his business** nothing to do with him – 7 **to remind sb** to tell someone that they wanted to do sth – 11 **heart-shaped** in the form of a heart – 12 **bangs** hair that is cut above the eyes – 13 **forehead** the part of the head above the eyes – 18 **anxiety** feeling of nervousness or worry – 19 **unwelcome** not wanted – 27 **honest** truthful and open

She looked straight into his eyes. "You know, I could be rather angry. A complete stranger interfering in somebody else's affairs! It isn't usual, is it?"

"No, it isn't. But when I see somebody I think looks especially nice, I try to make friends – to see if I was right! No, but I do think you're in trouble, and I would like to help you if you'll let me."

She smiled. "Well you're honest! But you can't help me, I'm afraid, and I'd rather not talk about it, if you don't mind. I'll have that cup of coffee, though. Let's go and sit at a table. It's more comfortable."

Betty smiled to herself as she came to take their order. She would have liked to be in the girl's place, instead of serving her. But Kev had never been interested in her.

"Just two cups of coffee, please, Betty," Kevin said.

"OK, sir!" Betty said.

"Where do you come from?" Kevin asked the girl.

"New York."

16 **to interfere** to get mixed up in – 16 **affairs** *here:* business – 18 **especially** really – 23 **I'd rather not** I'd prefer not to – 27 **instead of** in place of

"Is that where you've come from now?"

"No. I'm still at school. I go to a boarding school twenty miles from Niagara. It's called Saint Cecilia's. Have you heard of it?"

"No. Is it one of those schools for rich girls?"

"Yes, but I hate it! If I wasn't able to read a lot of books, I don't know what I'd do."

"Have you run away from school, then?"

"No – it's the first day of the vacation."

She looked straight into his eyes. He leaned across the table.

"I'm Kevin Patterson. I live here in Niagara Falls. What's your name?"

"Cathy."

"Cathy who?"

"Cathy O'Brien."

They shook hands.

"Why won't you tell me what's the matter, Cathy?"

She did not answer for a moment, and then she spoke in such a low voice that he could hardly hear her. "Because if you knew, it might get you into serious trouble."

"I'll risk it. Please tell me! I don't like mysteries between friends."

"No. Please don't talk about it again." She looked out the window. "Don't you get tired of that awful noise – the Falls, I mean?"

"No, I guess we're used to it."

Betty brought two cups and poured in the coffee. Then, when Kevin did not look at her, she gave him a kick under the table. Kevin did not notice.

"How is it your eyes are blue when your hair is so dark, Cathy?"

"That often happens with Irish people. My mother was Irish. My father was an Irish American."

"Are your parents dead?"

---

2 **boarding school** a school where students live – 8 **vacation** *(AE)* holiday(s) – 9 **to lean** to move your body in a direction – 18 **hardly** almost not – 23 **awful** terrible – 25 **I guess** I expect, I imagine

"Yes. My mother died when my brother was born. I was ten then. My father married again, but he died when I was twelve."

"So you were brought up by your stepmother?"

She hesitated. "Well, I live with her. My brother is luckier. He's been brought up by my grandmother in Charleston, South Carolina. I hardly ever see him, and that makes me very sad."

"How old are you, Cathy?"

"Seventeen."

"Me too. I'll be eighteen next month. I've just left high school. I'm going to be a guide for Swift's Tours in New York for a year. Do you know them?"

She shook her head.

"I know New York well. I spent a year there when I was fifteen. We must meet. I'll be there next week. Tell me your address."

She looked down at the table. "No, I don't think that would be safe. But I'd love to see you. Why don't you give me *your* address?"

"Sure!" Kevin answered.

Suddenly he saw her freeze. The coffee-shop door had opened, and a middle-aged woman was coming towards them. Her face was heavy, and her straight brown hair had been cut short above her ears. She wore long black boots and a thick grey coat. She looked rather like a soldier.

"Your stepmother?" Kevin said in a low voice.

"Yes."

The stepmother stood beside Cathy, who sat quite still, not looking at her.

"I told you to meet me at the car at 4.30. It's now 5 o'clock. What have you been doing?"

She looked suspiciously at Kevin. "Who's this?" she asked Cathy.

"A Canadian friend," Cathy answered.

"You make friends quickly, I see! What's his name?"

---

3 **to bring up** to look after and educate (a child) – 3 **stepmother** a woman married to your father (not your mother) – 4 **to hesitate** to pause – 17 **sure** of course, certainly – 19 **middle-aged** between young and old – 25 **quite still** without moving – 29 **suspiciously** without trust

"Rob Masterman," Cathy lied, without a moment's hesitation.

Kevin got up and held out his hand, but the stepmother let it hang in the air. She looked at him for a long time, as if she wanted to remember his face. Then she took Cathy's arm and pulled her to her feet.

"Come on, child! We're late."

Holding Cathy's arm firmly in hers, she marched to the door. Cathy turned back and looked hard at Kevin. He was sure that she was asking him for help. He nodded his head, trying to make her understand that he would look for her in New York. She disappeared, and a moment later Kevin heard the roar of a powerful car. The stepmother was clearly in a hurry. But where was she going?

"What was all that about?" Betty asked. "Who was that awful woman?"

"Her stepmother."

---

27 **roar** loud noise

"Poor kid!"

"You're darned right!"

"Look!" Betty said suddenly. "She has left her bag behind."

Kevin picked it up. It was quite an ordinary bag, black and rather old.

"Let's see what's inside," Betty said

Kevin opened it and found only a handkerchief and a purse with a few coins in it, and a key. That was all.

"It must be the key to her front door in New York – in Manhattan, the Bronx, Brooklyn, Queens? Where could it be?"

"Why do you want to find her?"

"Because she's rather special, I think, and she's in some sort of trouble. I'd like to help her."

"She probably just hates her stepmother. You can't do anything about that."

"No! I'm sure she's in serious trouble."

"You've been watching too much TV! Cops and robbers!"

"Maybe you're right, Betty. Give me my check, please."

He paid and went back to his empty home. His mother was in Toronto. She was not coming back. It would be almost a week before he was in New York. That was too long to wait. He sat down at the phone and called Aunt Bella.

"OK if I come on Thursday instead of Sunday, Aunt Bella?"

"Of course, honey!" his aunt said. "Come any time you like. It can't be very nice living alone in that house."

---

2 **you're darned right!** *(AE, informal)* you're absolutely right – 7 **handkerchief** a square of material to blow your nose on – 7 **purse** *(AE)* handbag – 17 **cop** *(AE, informal)* police officer – 17 **robber** sb who steals – 18 **check** *(AE)* bill

Think about it...

?

Kevin's mother thinks it is none of his business whether she marries the Toronto businessman. Do you agree? What would you say to her?

Kevin finds Cathy's bag and opens it. Do you think he has a right to do this? What would you do?

2 Journey to New York

The next day, Kevin packed his rucksack and put Cathy's key in an inside pocket of his jacket. Then he went to the bank. He changed all the money he had into American dollars, and then walked to the bridge which crossed the border.

It was a warm spring afternoon when he crossed the bridge to the American side of the Falls. Far below he could see the little ship, *Maid of the Mist*, crowded with tourists, moving slowly towards the world's greatest waterfall. He had once wanted to be captain of the *Maid of the Mist* …

The Immigration Officer on the American side of the bridge knew him and let him through at once. He went into a truck stop and asked if anyone would give him a lift to New York.

"OK, kid, I'll take you," said a cheerful young Texan on his way to New Jersey.

They drove through the night, stopping twice at all-night truck stops. Adam was in a hurry and, unlike most of the cars

---

19 **border** the line between two countries – 22 **crowded** full of – 23 **once** *here*: at one time – 25 **immigration officer** person who checks passports at a border – 26 **truck stop** *(AE)* filling station with café for lorry drivers – 28 **cheerful** happy, full of energy

they passed, drove much faster than the 65 mph speed limit.
They reached the suburbs of New York City at 6 o'clock in the
morning.

"What part of New York do you want, kid?"

"Greenwich Village."

"OK. I'll take you as far as the George Washington Bridge."

He stopped near the bridge.

"This is it, kid."

"Thanks, Adam."

"See you, Kev."

Kevin walked across the great bridge. The sun was coming
up, but was not yet shining on the broad Hudson River. As
he walked slowly through Fort Washington Park, a policeman
came up behind him.

"What's a kid like you doin' here at this hour?"

"Just walking. I'm allowed to, aren't I?"

"Sure, it's allowed! Where you from?"

"Niagara Falls, Canada."

"Let's see your passport."

The policeman looked at it carefully and then gave it back to
him. "How did you get here?"

"On a truck."

"Hitch-hiking on freeways is not allowed. You know that?"

"No, I didn't."

More and more commuters were beginning to cross the George
Washington Bridge and drive on down the Parkway to the center
of Manhattan. Americans start work early.

"If you're hoping to get work, you know what'll happen to you
if you don't have a permit?"

"I do have a permit."

He showed it to the policeman.

---

1 **65 mph speed limit** you can't drive faster than 65 miles per hour – 10 **see you!** bye! –
12 **broad** wide – 23 **to hitch-hike** to travel for free by getting into sb's car – 23 **freeway**
(AE) motorway – 25 **commuter** a person who travels regularly between two places

The policeman looked at Kevin's clothes and his well-cut blond hair.

"Why didn't you come by air, or by Greyhound? You don't look poor."

"I didn't have enough money."

"Where you goin' now, then?"

"To my aunt's house in Greenwich Village."

"OK, but don't do anything stupid while you're in New York," he said, and walked away through the park.

It was now nearly 7 o'clock. Kevin walked to the nearest subway station on 168th Street and Broadway. He bought an electronic fare card for 10 dollars for the first days, thinking he'd probably buy a weekly pass when he was working. He went through the turnstile and down to the trains. It was easy to get lost in the subway until you understood it, but it was the cheapest way of traveling. For the same fare you could travel from one end

---

19 **Greyhound** bus line in USA, Canada and Mexico (often the cheapest way to travel) – 27 **subway** *(AE)* underground railway – 28 **fare card** pass for bus and subway – 30 **turnstile** gate that turns as you go through it – 30 **to get lost** to not find your way

of New York to the other and transfer to buses, too. An express roared through the station on the center track and a few minutes later the local train came in. It was rush hour, so he had to push his way into the crowded car. He changed at Columbus Circle and finally came up at 53rd Street and Fifth Avenue. He had decided not to go straight to Aunt Bella's. He wanted to feel what New York was like again. He had spent a very happy year there.

As he wandered among the people on Fifth Avenue, Kevin began to think of Cathy. He looked for her among the hurrying crowd. Strange things did sometimes happen! Two well-dressed African-Americans crossed in front of him. And then he saw her. She was only a few yards in front of him. He knew it was her, the way she walked, the dark hair which fell below her ears. He called out, "Cathy!" and began to run. As he came up beside her, a pretty woman of about forty turned and smiled at him when she saw his disappointment.

"Excuse me!" he said.

He left Fifth Avenue and looked for a cheap coffee shop where he could have breakfast. Aunt Bella's breakfasts were not large enough for him. He sat at the counter and ordered two fried eggs, over easy, with hash browns and a cup of coffee, which the waitress filled up three times at no extra cost.

"You're Canadian, aren't you?" she asked. "I can tell from the accent."

"Yeah!" he replied. "Niagara Falls."

It was 9 o'clock, time to go and say "Hi!" to Aunt Bella. He went down into the subway again and got out at Washington Square. The streets of Greenwich Village were quiet and empty compared with the crowds and noise of the great Avenues. Children were playing beneath the trees of the Square, while students hurried across it to their lectures in New York University.

---

1 **to transfer to sth** to change over to sth – 2 **track** *(AE)* railway line (also platform) – 3 **rush hour** time of the day when there is the most traffic – 4 **car** *(AE)* (railway) carriage – 21 **over easy** *(AE)* egg fried on both sides – 21 **hash browns** *(AE)* a kind of fried potato eaten at breakfast – 31 **lecture** lessons at university

He stood for a moment under the great Washington Arch and
looked up Fifth Avenue. It was very broad and straight, and was
so long that he could not see to the end of it. It ran right down
the center of Manhattan. Then he walked down the little tree-
lined street where Aunt Bella had her apartment. The house had
only three floors, and Aunt Bella owned the top two. He climbed
the steps to the street door on the second floor and rang the bell.

When Aunt Bella saw him standing there, she threw her arms
around him.

"Kevin! It's lovely to see you. Have you had breakfast? Of
course you have! I'd forgotten. You don't like my breakfasts, do
you? I'll have to get some more eggs. How's your mother?"

"She's going to marry that guy!"

Aunt Bella and her sister-in-law were not great friends.

"Well, if it makes her happy …"

Aunt Bella was between forty and fifty. She liked to change the
color of her hair. At the moment it was red, and her chocolate-

---

19 **tree-lined** with trees on both sides – 20 **apartment** *(AE)* flat (Wohnung) – 28 **guy** man

colored shirt hung over bright purple pants. People loved her.
She spent her whole life and much of her money – she was not
rich – in trying to help the many different ethnic groups of the
great city.

"Just come and go as you like," she said. "You won't see much
of me. You know that."

Kevin smiled. He understood his aunt and loved her.

"Which group are you working for now, Aunt Bella?"

"The Puerto Ricans. Their life is very difficult. Many of them
can't get jobs because they don't speak English well enough. You
know, some Americans are unpleasant to people who don't speak
English well. Here's a spare door key. The bed's ready in the little
room upstairs. Now I have to write a letter."

She sat down at her desk. Kevin admired his aunt and her
enthusiasm. There were so many different ethnic groups in New
York. There were whole streets where Italians lived together. In
fact, more Italians lived in New York than in Rome, more Jews
than in Tel Aviv. There were more than two million blacks and
Puerto Ricans. Then there were the Irish Americans, who still
called themselves Irish and still hated the English.

He sat on the couch for a while, dreaming. Then he fetched
the telephone book which had names beginning with 'O'. He soon
shut the book. It was hopeless. There were hundreds of O'Briens.
He shut the book with such a bang that Aunt Bella looked up
from her desk.

"What's the matter, Kev? Who are you looking for in that
telephone book? A girlfriend?"

"Well, sort of."

He told his aunt everything that had happened and she listened
very carefully. He was sure she would have some very useful ideas.
She thought for a moment, Then she suddenly said, "You were

1 **pants** *(AE)* trousers – 11 **unpleasant** not nice – 12 **spare** extra – 14 **to admire sb** to
like and respect sb very much – 15 **enthusiasm** positive energy – 21 **fetch** get – 28 **sort
of** in a way

talking about a boarding school she went to in upstate New York.
Did she tell you its name?"

"Yes. It was Saint something … something beginning with S
or C."

"Get me the Buffalo book," Aunt Bella said. "Thank you. Now
then …

Well, I can only see one boarding school beginning with 'Saint'.
Was it Saint Cecilia's?"

"Yes, it was. Aunt Bella, you're wonderful!"

"No, honey. I use my imagination. That's all!"

"Do you think they would really give us her home address?"

"They might not if you called. But if I called and said I was an
old friend of the family, I think they would."

"It's the vacation. Do you think anyone will still be there?"

"I think the secretary will still be there. Anyway, I'll try, honey."

"Thank you, Aunt Bella!"

Aunt Bella's voice, as she talked to the secretary, was all honey.

---

16 **upstate New York** northern part of N.Y. State – 25 **honey** *(AE)* darling, babe

"Oh, thank you so much, it's real kind of you. Not at all! Goodbye!"

She wrote the address down on a card and gave it to Kevin.

"You sure know how to act, Aunt Bella. I didn't know you were as good as that."

"I'm good at everything, honey!"

"You sure are!"

She became suddenly serious. "You say the girl is in trouble, Kev. You realize the neighborhood she lives in is not exactly nice? That part of the West Side can even be dangerous, especially at night. It's a poor neighborhood. Someone was murdered there the other night."

"I'll be careful, Aunt Bella."

"I know you, Kev. You don't know what the word means!"

"I'm nearly three years older now."

"Maybe, maybe! But I must finish my letter. I've found some books on New York which may be a help to you. They're on the table by the couch."

Think about it …

Kevin goes into a truck stop and asks if anyone can take him to New York.

Why do you think he does this? What are the risks of travelling like this? Would you do this? And what are the cheapest ways of travelling where you live?

---

1 real kind *(AE)* really nice – 11 **neighborhood** area to live in – 11 **to murder** to kill

3 The search for
Cathy begins

Aunt Bella blew him a kiss and left. He lay on the couch, turning
over the pages of a not very interesting book on New York. "New
York is held together by 25 bridges. The Brooklyn Bridge is the
oldest suspension bridge in the world …". He imagined he was on
Brooklyn Bridge with a party of tourists … "And did you know,
folks, that the engineer who built the Brooklyn Bridge died after
an accident while the bridge was being built? And later his son
became paralyzed? He stayed too long under the water while he
was examining the bottom of the bridge. But the bridge sure does
look pretty at night when all its lights are on …"

He turned over a few more pages … "You know, folks, there's
no place called the 'Big Apple'. New York is the Big Apple –
Rockefeller Center, Broadway, all the great Avenues, Harlem
with its poor areas, the United Nations building, Chinatown, the
Hudson River – the whole exciting, beautiful place called New
York. That's the Big Apple." He shut the book with a bang. He was
not afraid of being a guide. He liked people, and they liked him.

19 **suspension** hanging 21 **folks** *(AE)* people – 21 **engineer** sb who designs sth
technical – 23 **paralyzed** unable to move – 24 **examine** study

He got up and walked up and down the room. Then, making a quick decision, he called Cathy's number.

"Yes? Who is it?"

He recognized Mrs. O'Brien's voice at once.

"We met at Niagara Falls, do you remember?"

"You're Rob Masterman?"

"Er … yes, that's right. I promised Cathy I'd call her when I got to New York."

Mrs. O'Brien tried to stop him, but Kevin talked straight on.

"I wonder if I could talk to Cathy? You see, I'm starting work in three days' time. She …"

"I'm sorry," Mrs. O'Brien said in a hard voice, "Cathy doesn't want to see you. So please don't call again."

She put down the telephone without waiting for him to answer. He was more than ever sure that Cathy's trouble was something to do with her stepmother. He looked at his watch. It was 11.30. He decided to go to the apartment house and ask at the desk to see Cathy. He was sure that the stepmother would not allow him to see her, but he might learn something interesting.

He went out into the cool spring air. It was a beautiful day. The windows of the skyscrapers which rose high above the old red houses of Washington Square shone like jewels in the sunshine. He reached the subway station and went down to the trains. When the train came in there was only standing room, and he stood among a group of African-Americans and Puerto Ricans. Rich New Yorkers rarely take the subway.

At last he reached his station. He came out on Eighth Avenue. It was one of the poorer districts of Manhattan. He passed small stores and offices, bars and cheap restaurants. When he reached the street which he guessed led down to the O'Brien's apartment house on Eleventh Avenue, he turned left. At the bottom of the street he could see a big new building. It was

---

2 **decision** plan – 4 **to recognize sb** to know who sb is – 21 **skyscraper** very tall building – 29 **store** (AE) shop

not like other buildings in Manhattan. It was taller than all the buildings around it, but it was not a skyscraper. It was about thirty stories high and very wide. The houses along the street had been built in the mid-nineteenth century, so New Yorkers called them old. People with money had once lived in them, but now there were only poor whites and poor blacks. At the end of the street, opposite the high wall of the apartment house, the houses were empty and many of the doors and windows were broken. Eleventh Avenue was even less smart than Eighth Avenue. The buildings were three or four stories high, and all kinds of advertisements had been stuck on the walls.

The main entrance to the apartment house was on Eleventh Avenue. It was very different from what he had expected. He could see at once that the apartments belonged to people with money. Cathy must have a fine view of the Hudson River and

---

3 **story** *(AE)* / **storey** *(BE)* floor in a building – 9 **smart** elegant; neat and clean –
11 **advertisement** picture and text telling people why they should buy a product

the docks where the cruise liners lay, for the number of her apartment was 908, and that meant that it was on the ninth floor. He walked down Eleventh Avenue, trying to decide what to do. He reached the Lincoln Tunnel, one of the two great
5 tunnels connecting New York with New Jersey. Trucks, yellow cabs, Lincolns, Corvettes, traffic of all kinds, disappeared under the Hudson River. At last he decided to do what he had at first intended to do – ask to see Cathy.

Kevin went back to the apartment house and walked straight
10 through the glass doors into the lobby. He was surprised at what he saw. Between the lobby and the elevators there were two locked turnstiles which could only be opened by the people who lived there, or by the security guard. On the desk lay an open book and a telephone, and behind the desk stood a security guard who
15 looked as if he had once been a policeman. Kevin had never seen anything quite like this. He knew that in the smart apartment houses people had special locks on their doors, and little holes through which they could look at their visitors. He knew, too, that there were sometimes muggings in the elevators and even in
20 offices. But he had never heard of locked turnstiles before.

He went up to the security guard who, he was glad to find, gave him a friendly smile.

"What can I do for you, kid?"

"I'd like to see Cathy O'Brien, please."

25 "Oh, you would, would you? And who shall I say you are?"

Kevin was just going to say 'Rob Masterman', when he remembered his passport.

"Kevin Patterson," he said.

The guard held out his hand. "Come on, Kevin Patterson! Let's
30 see some I.D."

---

1 **docks** area where ships come in – 1 **cruise liner** big passenger vacation ships –
6 **cab** *(AE)* taxi – 6 **Lincoln, Corvette** American cars – 10 **lobby** entrance hall of hotel or
apartment building – 13 **security guard** sb who checks that people are allowed to go into
a building – 19 **mugging** robbery attack on the street – 30 **I.D.** (proof of) identity
(e.g. driver's license passport)

Kevin showed him his passport.

"OK! I'll call the apartment."

The guard picked up the phone. "That Mrs. O'Brien? There's a young man here who says his name is Kevin Patterson. He'd like to see Cathy … She's gone to find out if she'll see you," he told Kevin. "Mrs. O'Brien? She will see him? … She'll be down in a minute? Oh, sure! He'll wait!"

Kevin was very surprised, but said nothing. A few minutes later, he heard the elevator doors opening – and saw Mrs. O'Brien coming towards him on the other side of the turnstiles.

"Kevin Patterson! Rob Masterman! Did you really think you'd trick me with a false name?" She turned to the security guard. "Which is his real name?"

"His passport says Kevin Patterson."

"Can't you get it into your thick head that you aren't going to see my stepdaughter? Now just go away, and don't ever come back."

"Why? I think Cathy would like to see me."

"Don't talk to me like that!" she said angrily. Then she turned to the security guard. "Get rid of him, please!"

The guard, who was now no longer friendly, came from behind the desk, took Kevin by the arm and threw him out the door into the street.

"Next time you come round here, I'll call the police."

As Kevin got up, he saw through the glass doors an African-American standing in the middle of the lobby and staring at him. The man turned his back as soon as he saw Kevin looking at him. But Kevin knew that he would recognize him again at once, because he was completely bald.

He walked back up the street. The neighborhood was unpleasant, and he wanted to get out of it as quickly as possible.

---

12 **trick** make sb believe sth that isn't true – 15 **thick** stupid – 20 **get rid of sb** throw sb out 26 **to stare at sb** to look hard at sb – 29 **bald** without hair

There was no one in the lower part of the street, except a few
children playing among the empty, damaged houses. At the top
end, women were talking together on their doorsteps. They did
not turn and look at him as he passed. He crossed avenue after
avenue until he reached the Avenue of the Americas. Rockefeller
Center was quite near. He sat down under one of the big
sunshades and ordered a hot chocolate. There were people of
all kinds at the tables around him. There were young people in
jeans, like him. There were smartly dressed ladies who had come
to Manhattan to shop, and a few businessmen who had left their
skyscraper offices for a late coffee break.

Afterward he walked past Radio City Music Hall, which he
had visited many times during his earlier stay in New York. It
was built in the thirties, but was still one of the largest movie
houses in the world. It was showing the latest horror movie. He

29 afterward(s) after that – 32 latest most recent

remembered the great Wurlitzer organ, the largest of its kind in the world, and in the interval there were the Rockettes dancing girls, who danced with the discipline of well-trained soldiers. He stopped at a snack bar for a hot dog, and then walked up Broadway to Times Square, one of the most famous centers of New York. There were advertisements on all the buildings. There were also many movie houses with large, colored posters.

Further along Broadway, between Times Square and Lincoln Center, he passed the Swift's Tours office, where he would soon be working. He looked in the window and noticed the tours they were advertising, but he did not go in. By now his feet were sore, but he walked on to Lincoln Center, where he hoped to get tickets for a concert or an opera but they were all too expensive.

Kevin arrived back at Aunt Bella's at 4.30 and threw himself on the couch. Aunt Bella listened without a smile when he told her what had happened at the apartment house, and about the bald African-American in the lobby.

"Well, if you're sensible, which you're not, you'll have nothing more to do with Cathy O'Brien. Take her stepmother's warning seriously. I don't want to learn one day that my beloved nephew has been murdered."

Kevin sat up. "Are you being serious, Aunt Bella?"

"Completely! I know people talk too much about the dangers of New York. But there are gangs, and there are muggers, and sometimes ordinary people get hurt. It wouldn't surprise me if Cathy's stepmother had something to do with a gang."

"Perhaps you're right, Aunt Bella, but I don't think Cathy is part of it."

"Maybe not, but that doesn't make it any safer for you."

Kevin looked his aunt in the eyes. "Aunt Bella, you know I'm always honest with you. I'm going to go on finding out what I

---

1 **organ** musical instrument – 2 **interval** break in a performance – 11 **sore** painful – 18 **sensible** willing to do the right thing – 20 **beloved** sb you love – 24 **mugger** sb who attacks sb in the street

can. If I find out anything really dangerous, then I'll go to the police. I promise you! Try not to worry."

"OK," his aunt said. "I can't stop you, and I won't try, but you can't stop me worrying. All I can say is, 'good luck', and please ask me if you want any help."

They stared at each other without smiling, which did not happen very often. Then Kevin went up to his aunt and kissed her.

"I'll try and be careful, Aunt Bella. I promise you."

This time his aunt did smile. "You're quite your father's son. He was just as crazy as you!"

---

31 **to be your father's son** to be just like your father

Think about it...

Kevin is learning about New York for his new job
as a tour guide. If you were a tour guide where you
live, what would you want to tell people about?

The building where Cathy lives is very secure.
Why do you think that is? How safe is the
area you live in? What do you do to stay safe?

4 Kevin tries again

The next morning Kevin said to his aunt, "I'm going to the apartment house again. If something happens, I thought you would want to know … I'm sure it won't, but …"

Aunt Bella got up without a word, opened the telephone book and wrote down a number in her note book. "That's the nearest police precinct," she said. Her face was unsmiling.

"That's a good idea," Kevin replied.

Aunt Bella laughed. "Maybe you're not so like your father after all. He would have told me it was nothing to do with me!"

Kevin reached the apartment house at 10.30. This time he stood close to the wall of one of the empty buildings across the road. Black women and white women, some of them holding small children by the hand, came out the building with their

6 precinct *(AE)* police station for one area

shopping baskets. A big New York garbage truck stopped in front
of him and lifted the garbage from the sidewalk. But nothing
else passed either up or down the street. Children were running
in and out the empty houses, playing games. Time passed. He
looked at his watch. It was already 12.30, and he was getting
hungry. Did Mrs. O'Brien know that he was there? He looked up
at the shining wall of windows. Was her apartment on this side or
the other side of the building?

Kevin waited another half-hour and then decided to give up.
He was walking back up the street when he heard the sound of a
car behind him. He turned, but it was difficult to see the person
behind the driving wheel because the sun was shining on the
windshield. The car, a dirty ten-year-old Oldsmobile, was driving
on the wrong side of the road, beside the sidewalk on which he
was walking. It was less than twenty yards behind him. As he
looked back, the car turned quickly towards him, driving at great
speed. Kevin just had time to throw himself through the door
of one of the empty houses. The car hit the wall of the house,
but was thrown back onto the road again. It disappeared up the
street.

Kevin had cut his face and hands when he fell. There was dust
all over his clothes. There was dust in his eyes, too. He sat up
rubbing them. When his eyes were clear, he saw a young black
woman looking down at him.

"That man sure tried to kill you. He's crazy!"

"Can you tell me what he was like?"

"Sure! He's black, but he's got some white in him, too, and he
sure is bald!"

"Do you know him then?"

"Do I know him! Everyone knows him – everyone around here,
I mean."

---

1 **garbage** *(AE)* rubbish – 2 **sidewalk** *(AE)* path at the side of the street –
13 **windshield** *(AE)* windscreen *(BE)* window at the front of the car – 21 **dust** brown /
beige dirt – 23 **rub** try to clean with your hands

"Would you give evidence against him if the police caught him?"

"Oh, no, man! I couldn't do that. It would be kind of signing my death warrant. I'd say I never saw nothing. I sure am sorry, honey, but that's the way it is. Come with me. I'll clean you up."

Kevin followed her into her first floor apartment. She had two young children, and only two rooms. There was hardly any furniture in the apartment. To get hot water, she had to boil a kettle on the stove. When the water was hot enough, she cleaned his cuts and washed the dirt from his face.

"Maybe you ought to see a doctor," she said. "Those cuts are real bad."

"No, I'll be OK, thank you. You were real kind."

"You're welcome! Get well soon."

Kevin stopped in the doorway. "You couldn't tell me if he lives in the apartment house at the bottom of the street?"

"No, honey. I can't do that. Bye!" and she went inside and shut the door.

Kevin looked in every direction. There was no sign of the Oldsmobile. He walked fast until he reached Eighth Avenue. There, right on the corner, was the Oldsmobile. He noticed that there was a bus stop on the other side of the Avenue, for buses going uptown. He hid in a doorway and waited, hoping the driver had not seen him. A few moments later, the stop lights said "Walk", and he ran across the road just in time to jump on a bus before it moved off. He looked behind him. The Oldsmobile had made a U-turn and was moving slowly forward, keeping just behind the bus.

He put his electronic card in the slot, but he did not sit down. The driver shut the door and the bus moved off. The Oldsmobile

followed. They went round Columbus Circle, but after a few
blocks there was a traffic jam. A yellow cab had stopped in the
middle of the Avenue and the driver was examining the engine.
Kevin looked through the window and saw the trees of Central
5 Park rising above the traffic. He could only just see the hood of
the Oldsmobile and knew that the bald African-American could
not see him.

"Can I get off here?" he begged the driver.

"It's not a stop."

10 "Please, I've got to get off!"

The driver looked at the cuts on his face. "What have you done
to yourself?"

"I fell over."

"You should go to a doctor."

15 "Please, will you open the door?"

"OK, but be quick. This traffic jam isn't going on forever."

Kevin jumped off the bus and crossed the street, walking
through the jam of cars. As he entered the Park, he looked round.
He could not see the Oldsmobile anywhere. With luck, the driver
20 had not seen him get off the bus. He walked straight to the lake
and sat down on the grass, choosing a place where there were
other people. In summer the lake was crowded, but today there
were only two or three rowboats on the dark water. An elegantly
dressed girl rode by on horseback. At any other time, he would
25 have enjoyed sitting in Central Park. It was a great sports center
and playground for New Yorkers. It was at the ice rink here that he
had learned to skate, and he had many times rowed on the lake.
Little children screamed as they ran after each other round the
great, gray rocks. New York was built on rock, but the only rock
30 to be seen now was in Central Park. Two joggers ran by. Two old
people were finishing their lunch on the grass beside him. The
man got up and threw the plastic cups and plates into a trash can.

---

2 block (AE) buildings between two streets and two avenues – 5 hood (AE) metal part
that covers a car's engine – 8 to beg to ask anxiously – 26 ice rink an area with ice for
people to skate on – 27 to skate to walk and slide on ice – 32 trash can (AE) rubbish bin

5

10

15

Most Americans like public places to be clean and do not leave trash on the ground.

A half-hour later, Kevin got up. There was no sign of the African-American with the bald head. He decided to walk across the Park down the broad, tree-lined Mall. As he neared the Zoo at the far end, he happened to look round. The Mall was full of people. But among them he saw a bald black head. He began to run – past the Zoo and out of the Park into Grand Army Plaza. People were still sitting round the statue in the middle of the Plaza finishing their picnic lunches. He sat down among them and looked across to the Park. The heads of the two young people in front of him were so close together that he could not possibly be seen. This time he had a good view of the African-American. His skin was black, and he was bald, but he had the nose and lips of a white man. He was tall and looked strong, and he was well-dressed and wore a pair of gloves. Kevin was sure he would recognize him if he saw him again.

---

17 **trash** *(AE)* rubbish – 20 **Mall** *here:* broad path in Central Park

New York – Manhattan Island

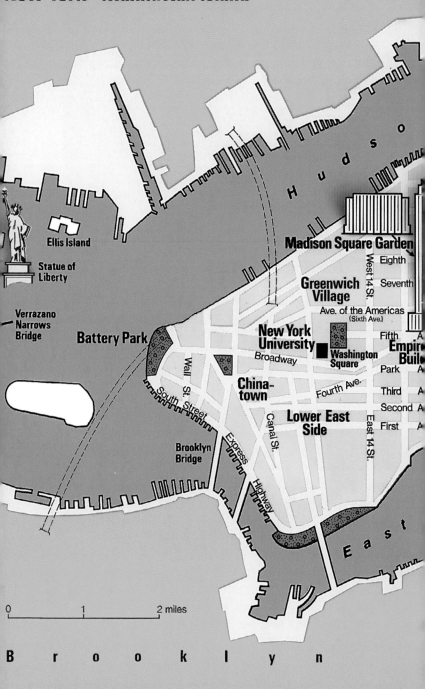

Hudso

Ellis Island

Statue of Liberty

Madison Square Garden

West 14 St.

Eighth

Seventh

Greenwich Village

Ave. of the Americas
(Sixth Ave.)

Verrazano Narrows Bridge

Battery Park

New York University

Fifth

Empire Buil

Wall St.

South Street

Broadway

Washington Square

Park A

China-town

Fourth Ave.

Third A

Canal St.

Second A

Lower East Side

East 14 St.

First A

Brooklyn Bridge

Express Highway

East

0   1   2 miles

B   r   o   o   k   l   y   n

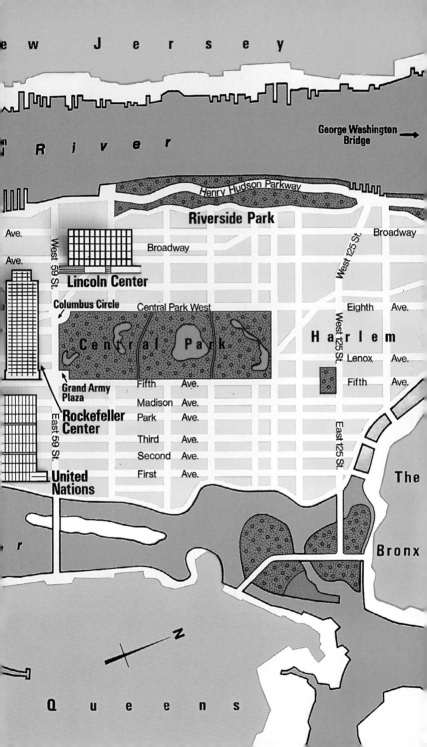

The man's eyes were searching the sidewalk. For some reason, he did not think of looking at the statue. Cars and cabs were stopping in front of the Plaza Hotel, one of New York's most expensive hotels. Kevin thought of hiding in the hotel. You can walk into most hotels in New York without being stopped by the doorman. He looked back at the Park. The man had gone. But he could be anywhere, and still waiting for him. Kevin was afraid to return to Greenwich Village at once. He did not want the man to discover where he lived. He was thinking not only of himself, but also of Aunt Bella.

He quickly crossed the street into Fifth Avenue and walked uptown, past the tall apartment houses where many of the rich New Yorkers lived. He looked behind him every few minutes. Why had the man tried to kill him? Kevin's eyes searched everywhere, but he could not see any bald African-Americans. At last he turned round and walked back again. The guy had disappeared.

From Fifty-Ninth Street down, Fifth Avenue has some of the smartest and most expensive stores in Manhattan. A young woman came out of a store wearing smart new clothes and diamond rings on her fingers. Kevin wandered about midtown Manhattan, past modern skyscrapers which he found very beautiful. They were all so different from each other. Every few minutes he hid in a doorway as close to the entrance as possible. Once he hid for five minutes in a subway station, but the African-American did not appear. Tired and anxious, he went down into one of the underground shopping malls. It was good to escape from the traffic, and he walked through the mall until he reached a café on a terrace where there were small trees and running

---

6 **doorman** sb who stands at the doors of the building often to protect it –
26 **anxious** worried, nervous – 27 **mall** *(AE)* here: shopping area without traffic

water. The sun streamed through a glass roof high above him. He sat down on a chair and ordered a coke, which he drank slowly. He looked around him, but could not see the bald man. He began to feel better. His neighbor was a middle-aged man with rather long hair and an old jacket. Opposite him sat an elegant young woman with her smart little girl. The café itself was smart, but the prices were not high and anybody could sit there as long as they liked.

At last Kevin decided to go home. When he reached the subway station, he hid once more near the entrance. He stayed in hiding for ten minutes, but the African-American still did not appear. When he got home, Aunt Bella was there and he told her what had happened.

"You'll have to go to the police, honey. This isn't the kind of job for boys. Look at those cuts on your face!"

"I haven't enough evidence to give the police, Aunt Bella. The young woman who saw that guy tried to kill me said she wouldn't give evidence against him. She hates him, I'm sure, but she's afraid. I don't think the security guard in the apartment house knows anything either. The police just wouldn't believe someone like me."

"Well, I don't think you ought to go near that apartment house again."

"I won't, Aunt Bella – at least not for the next few days. I'm starting work on Monday."

---

1 **to stream** *here:* to shine strongly – 16 **evidence** sth to show that sth happened

Think about it...

> Kevin has obviously become involved in a dangerous world. Do you think he should get out now or continue to find out what is going on?

Aunt Bella wants him to go to the police. Make a note of some reasons why he should or shouldn't go to the police.

Go to the police	Don't go to the police

5 The guide

On Monday Kevin arrived early at the office. Mr. Swift was there
to welcome him and decided to tell him about some of the people
and the problems he might meet. Mr. Swift then acted the part
of a dumb tourist who asked stupid questions, and after that the
part of a tourist who thought he knew more than the guide. Mr.
Swift liked the way Kevin answered all the questions. Kevin was
quick and he had a nice sense of humor. He also knew a lot about
New York.

"Your aunt was right. She always is!" he said. "And you seem to
know New York as well as a New Yorker. Still, for the first week
I'm putting you with Mrs Richter – or Debbie, as we call her.
You'll like her, and she'll help you a lot."

For the first few days, Kevin hardly had time to think about
Cathy, though once or twice his heart almost stopped when
he thought he saw the bald African-American. He enjoyed the
job. He soon became friends with pretty, young Debbie Richter,
who invited him to supper to meet her husband, Earle. One day

---

19 **dumb** *here:* stupid – 22 **sense of humor** sb's feeling for fun

Debbie and Kevin had to take a party of Texans up the Empire State Building. At Debbie's suggestion, Kevin did the talking. "It will give you practice," she said.

"OK," he said.

He felt a little nervous at first, but not for long.

"You folks think it's the tallest building in New York, don't you? … Well, you're right. The World Trade Center, which was built in 1973, was the highest building until September 11, 2001, when terrorists destroyed its twin towers. But this old girl held the record for over thirty years – the tallest building in the world. … Yes, sir, there is a skyscraper in Chicago that is taller than the old World Trade Center. And did you know that the tallest buildings in the world are now in Asia? They'll be reaching the moon before long!"

The express elevators in the Empire State Building are very fast. They travel eighty floors in less than one minute.

"Oh, dear!" one old lady cried.

"Don't worry, ma'am!" Kevin said. "This elevator has never in all its life killed a Texan!"

When it was all over, Debbie laughed, "You act the clown very well," she said. "They liked you!"

That evening he decided to risk it and go back to the apartment house on Eleventh Avenue. He told Aunt Bella, who tried to persuade him not to go. This time he walked up and down the far side of the Avenue for an hour. He hoped that he might see Cathy, or possibly the bald African-American. He had on different clothes and was wearing a cap, and as it was getting dark, he did not think the man would recognize him. He had just decided to leave, when a young boy dressed in smart clothes got out of a large chauffeur-driven limousine and walked up and

1 party group – 9 to hold the record to be the best at – 15 elevator (AE) / lift (BE) sth that takes people up and down the floors of a building quickly – 18 ma'am (AE) madam (in conversation) – 24 to persuade to give sb arguments why sth is a good or bad idea – 30 chauffeur-driven with a (private) driver

down the sidewalk not far from the apartment house. The boy
could hardly be more than fourteen. A moment later, the bald
guy came through the lobby doors. He was about to stop a cab,
when he saw the limousine on the other side of the street. He ran
across and began to shout angrily at the teenager. At last the boy,
after looking anxiously up and down the sidewalk, persuaded
the bald man to get into the limousine. Kevin moved back into a
doorway as the car drove off.

He walked home slowly, thinking of all the things he had seen
and heard. He was beginning to fit together what he knew and
to try and make some sense of it all: he knew Cathy was in some
kind of trouble and that she was afraid of her stepmother. Why?
And why didn't Cathy's stepmother want Cathy to see him?
Perhaps she was afraid Cathy would tell him something – but
what? Why, of course, something about her stepmother! Well,
certainly Cathy's stepmother didn't have very pleasant friends –
that bald guy, for example, who had tried to kill him. So this
'something' about Cathy's stepmother must be quite serious.
Kevin thought again about the teenager in the big limousine. The
way he acted was suspicious, too. In fact, anyone who knew that
creepy bald guy must be suspicious. But what was going on?

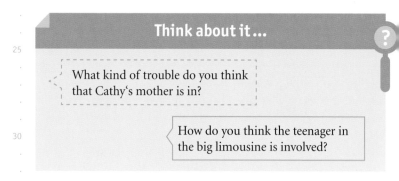

Think about it…

What kind of trouble do you think
that Cathy's mother is in?

How do you think the teenager in
the big limousine is involved?

---

10 **to fit together** to put together – 20 **suspicious** strangely – 21 **creepy**
(AE, informal) nasty

*

Next day he told Aunt Bella over a quick cup of coffee what he had seen and what he had thought about the night before.

Aunt Bella looked worried. "Listen, honey," she said, "this sounds real bad. I think your Mrs. O'Brien has something to do with a drug gang. It all fits, and this last piece of information makes me doubly sure. That kid, with the smart clothes and the big car, sounds like one of the teenage dealers who are so big in New York just now."

"But a teenager, Aunt Bella!"

"Don't be surprised, Kev. Because they're teenagers, they think they'll have an easier time in the courts, so they're prepared to risk anything. They can make a fortune. Why, I heard of one Puerto Rican girl who's only eighteen and she lives in a big apartment, wears the smartest clothes, has a chauffeur-driven

---

24 **big** *(AE, informal)* important, successful – 24 **dealer** sb who buys and sells sth –
29 **fortune** *here:* a lot of money

car, everything." Aunt Bella's voice was serious. "Please be very careful, honey."

That day Kevin and Debbie took a large party on a visit to the Statue of Liberty. The boat left every hour from Battery Park, a small public garden right at the end of Manhattan. On the way to Battery Park they walked down the narrow canyon of Wall Street, the world-famous business center of New York. About twenty of the younger members of the party said they were sure one of the great banks was a palace, and they marched in to have a look.

"I know they're only having fun, but get 'em out, Kev!" Debbie said.

"Come on, all of you!" Kevin said sharply. "You're not welcome here. Please get out at once!"

A woman in a gray coat was standing at one of the counters. She was holding a thick wad of dollar bills – Kevin guessed they were hundred dollar bills. His eyes met hers. It was Mrs. O'Brien. There was no doubt that Mrs. O'Brien was startled by this unexpected meeting. Kevin stared at the wad of bills and then left.

---

6 **canyon** narrow valley – 20 **wad** a thick bundle (of banknotes) – 27 **startled** surprised and frightened – 28 **unexpected** not planned

When they reached Battery Park, Kevin and Debbie sat down, glad of the twenty minutes they would have to wait for the boat. Some of the party went down to the water's edge and pointed out the sights. Others lined up at the Park's comfort station. A large cruise ship was just passing under the great suspension bridge of the Verrazano Narrows, on its way out to the Atlantic. Debbie was staring at Ellis Island, which lay between Manhattan and New Jersey. They looked at each other.

"You're very dreamy today, Kev. What are you thinking of?" Debbie asked.

"You tell me what you're thinking about first," Kevin said.

"I was remembering what Earle's grandmother told me about Ellis Island – how awful it was for her. She was a German from Cologne."

During the late nineteenth and early twentieth centuries, altogether eight million immigrants were held on Ellis Island, waiting their turn with the doctors. Few of these immigrants could speak English. The overworked doctors, who were not always kind, had to examine each one of them, because no one who was ill was allowed into the U.S.A.

"Earle's grandmother had an infectious disease. They let her through in the end, but her brother, who had nothing the matter with him, was sent back to Germany because he coughed once or twice."

"Well, it's an historic monument now," Kevin said.

There must have been pretty Irish immigrants who looked like Cathy, Kevin thought, and some of them must have had a hard time. The Irish were not at all liked at first in New York. Most of them were uneducated and very poor.

4 **to line up** *(AE)* to queue – 4 **comfort station** *(AE)* (public) toilet – 13 **awful** terrible – 17 **immigrant** sb who moves to a country – 21 **infectious disease** an illness that you can give to another person – 25 **historic monument** sth important that reminds people of an event in history – 29 **uneducated** without schooling

At that moment the boat for the Statue of Liberty came in, and they got up.

"I'm a bad sailor," an old lady said. "Do you think I'll be sick?"

"Look at the water, ma'am," Kevin said without a smile. "It's as calm as a lake."

They all hurried to get places on the boat.

"Kevin, what's the matter with you today?" asked Debbie. "What's happened to your sense of humor?"

"I don't have a sense of humor today," he said. "I'm very worried, Debbie. I'll tell you about it when we're free."

When they landed, an old man came up to them. "Do you think I could walk to the top?" he asked.

"No, I wouldn't if I were you," Debbie said. "There are 167 steps. I'd take the elevator. You'll have quite a few steps to climb when you leave the elevator."

A small boy ran up to Kevin. "Can I climb up the torch?" he asked.

"Sure," Kevin replied, "but first see if you can reach the top of the lady's crown before us. Come on, Debbie!"

---

5 **to be a bad sailor** to often be sea-sick – 28 **torch** sth you can hold that produces light

Kevin led the way. At the top, people crowded round him to ask questions.

"Who built the statue?"

"It was a gift from the French."

"The French? Why the French?"

"As a mark of friendship between the two countries."

"I didn't know there was any friendship!"

"You look surprised! The French helped the Americans against the British in the Revolutionary War, you know."

"Was it built, then, immediately after the Revolutionary War?"

"No, not until 1886."

They returned to Battery Park, where a bus was waiting for them. When the bus had delivered them all to their hotels, Debbie said to Kevin, "It's 6.30. Let's go and have something to eat at a fast food restaurant. Then you can tell me what's worrying you."

The place was clean and cheap. Debbie and Kevin stood at the counter.

"Beefburgers?" Kevin asked.

"OK," Debbie replied.

"Beefburgers and French fries for two," Kevin said. "And two coffees."

"To go?" the girl asked.

"No, to eat here."

The food was passed over the counter in styrofoam boxes. The knives and forks were plastic, and so were the coffee cups. There were trash cans in the restaurant into which the customers threw everything left at the end of the meal, including all the plastic material.

They sat down at a table against the wall. While they were eating their beefburgers, Kevin told Debbie everything that had happened since his meeting with Cathy at Niagara Falls. She listened without saying a word. Then suddenly she said in a low

---

6 **mark** sign – 20 **French fries** *(AE)* / *(BE)* **chips** long thin sticks of potato –
24 **styrofoam**® non-recycable material used in the past to serve food

voice, "Don't look, but there's a bald African-American sitting at a table on the other side of the room. He's with a strange-looking kid who can't be more than fourteen or fifteen. But he's wearing a smart business suit, and he's smoking a big cigar!"

Kevin kept his voice low. "That's Baldie all right! The kid must be the dealer he rode off with in the limousine last night."

"But a kid of that age!"

"I know. I told my Aunt Bella about the kid and the chauffeur-driven car. She said that teenage dealers take risks because they think they won't be sent to prison. She said they can make fortunes."

Debbie suddenly picked up all the trash from the table and went over to the trash can which stood a few feet from the black's table. She pushed the pieces in one by one, very slowly, plates, cups, knives, forks, spoons. Then she came and sat down again. Kevin had kept his face turned to the wall.

"Baldie's name is Johnnie," she said in a low voice. "Johnnie said to the kid, 'Meet you at the house then, at 8 o'clock.'"

"He didn't say where?"

"No," Debbie replied. "The kid's just gone out the door, and Johnnie's getting ready to leave."

Kevin leaned across the table. "Debbie," he said, "Johnnie once followed me. Now I'm going to follow him."

"Kev! That's dangerous and stupid. Why don't you go to the Precinct and ask to talk to the Lieutenant? People are often very unfair about the cops. They do a difficult job, and they do it well."

"I'll go when I'm ready, Debbie. I just don't have enough evidence yet. Anyway, there's one thing that worries me terribly. Does the stepmother know that Cathy knows? If she does, then Cathy could be in awful danger. She and her stepmother hate each other – I'm sure they do. It doesn't seem as if Cathy's been to the police. I'd like to know why. It could be something she's afraid of, Debbie. Could you call my aunt if I'm not …"

"Kev, he's getting up now!" She put her hand on his. "Be sensible, if that's possible. He's just thrown his trash into the trash can, and now he's going out the door."

"Thanks a lot, Debbie," Kevin said, getting up. "See you!"

"I'll call your aunt, Kev. Bye! And good luck!"

? Think about it …

It looks like Aunt Bella was right. Why do you think the boy was interested in working with Johnnie? What risks is he taking?

In many countries children and teenagers cannot be punished for crimes they commit. How fair do you think this is?

---

7 lieutenant *(AE) here:* chief police officer

6 A trip to Harlem

Johnnie was walking uptown along the sidewalk. Finally he
turned up West 34th Street and went into Madison Square
Garden, where a big match between two heavyweight boxers was
going to take place the following evening. Kevin had often been
to this big sports arena to watch basketball and hockey matches.
Johnnie came out again. He looked angry, and Kevin guessed
that there were no tickets left. Johnnie walked up Seventh Avenue
to Broadway and Times Square. In Times Square he examined
the advertisements outside the movie theaters and then finally
entered the subway. Kevin followed him and got into the next car
without being seen. But after a few stations they were already in
Harlem, and he had the feeling that he was the only white person
in the car. In the corner on the other side of the car there were

---

21 match game or fight where two teams or people play against each other –
21 heavyweight (boxer) in the heaviest class

two big black youths who kept looking at him and talking to one another in a low voice.

Kevin had seen Harlem once from a train that was on its way to Grand Central Station. Some parts were very poor-looking. Whole blocks of buildings seemed to be empty, with the windows broken or boarded up, but you could see from the lights that some people still lived there.

At last, at 125th Street and Lenox Avenue, Johnnie got out. The two youths got out too, and ran up the steps in front of Kevin. Johnnie walked away from the station. Kevin hesitated a second before following him. He was now in the middle of Harlem, and it was getting dark. This was a part of New York where his aunt had told him not to go. Debbie, too, had warned him to keep out of Harlem. "Many of the people who live there are very poor," she had said, "and where there is poverty there is crime."

Johnnie walked west along 125th Street for a block and then turned north. Kevin was glad he did not have far to go. Johnnie entered a house, smaller than most, in 127th Street, one block from the station. There was a street lamp in front of the door, so that Kevin could see quite clearly the comings and goings. A large yellow Mercedes stopped under the street lamp. A girl in a leather coat got out. She turned her head, and Kevin saw that she could not be more than sixteen. Altogether ten people walked through the door, and all of them were certainly under twenty-one. So this must be the meeting the strange-looking kid had told Johnnie about in the fast food restaurant.

Kevin made a note of the number of the house and turned back to the subway station. Two young black men stood in the entrance. They were the youths he had seen in the subway car. Kevin was scared. Were they going to mug him? Then he noticed a police car on the other side of 125th Street and crossed when the "Walk" sign came on. He had his fare card ready and ran

---

1 **youth** young person – 6 **to board sth up** to put pieces of wood over sth to cover it – 10 **to hesitate** to pause before doing sth – 15 **poverty** state of being very poor – 30 **to mug** to attack

through the turnstile. He was glad when he got down to the trains and saw that the youths hadn't followed him.

When he reached home soon after 9.30, Aunt Bella was out. He made himself a cup of hot chocolate and sat down on the couch. Did Cathy's stepmother really have something to do with a drug gang? If so, he must find Cathy quickly. He took her key from his pocket. He felt quite sure now that it was the key to her apartment. He'd find a way to get in. He must, he had to. By the time Aunt Bella came in, he had gone to bed.

The following day Kevin was free. Aunt Bella had just gone out when the telephone rang. He picked up. A girl's voice said, "Hello! Who's that?"

"Kevin Patterson speaking."

"It's Cathy, Kevin. Do you remember? We met at the coffee shop in Niagara Falls."

"Do I remember you, Cathy! You know I do! I've been having quite an interesting time trying to find you again!"

She spoke fast, telling him what had happened to her since. She had discovered that her stepmother was a kind of go-between in the drug business – between the big boss who smuggled the stuff from South America, and an African-American who sold it to dealers in Harlem.

"Is he bald and called Johnnie?"

"Yes! How on earth did you know that?"

She sounded frightened. He told her in a few words what had happened to him.

"Are you in any danger, Cathy?"

"No – not yet – but I'm afraid to call the police, because my stepmother has threatened to kill my brother if I do. She has connections in Charleston."

"How did you find out that she was in the drug racket?"

"It was between school and Niagara. She had to stop several times at a gas station to go to the restroom. She wasn't feeling at all well, and once she forgot to take her bag with her. It was open, so I looked inside, and I saw a letter. Of course I read it. I had always been suspicious that she was a crook, and in the letter I learned we were going to meet the big boss himself in Montreal, the man she gets the drugs from."

"You have his name and address?"

"Yes."

"Wonderful! Where are you calling from, Cathy?"

"From the apartment. She locks me in, and I can't open the door from the inside. And she told me that if I used the phone, she'd know every word I said because the room is bugged. I searched and searched, and today I found the bug. It's very, very small. I've taken it down and hidden it somewhere where it can't hear anything! It's OK, I'm sure, but I'll have to put it back."

"But how did you know my phone number?"

"I remembered that you'd said something about Swift's Tours. I called them. You weren't there, so they gave me your home number."

"Cathy, tell me, is Johnnie, that bald guy, your stepmother's partner?"

"Yes. He lives on the floor below us."

"I have your key, Cathy. You left your bag in the coffee shop, remember?"

"Yes. I guessed you must have it. It's a special key to the apartment. She gave it to me about two years ago, when we were 'friends'. Now, Kev, I've something very important to say. I've written it down, so I won't forget it. If you don't want to do what I ask, you must say so honestly."

"I'll do it, Cathy!"

"No, wait, Kev. Do you have a pencil and paper?"

---

2 **gas station** (AE) petrol station – 2 **restroom** (AE) toilet – 5 **crook** criminal – 13 **to be bugged** there is a bug, a small technical device, in the room which means that sb can listen to any conversation there

"Yes."

"I'll speak very slowly so that you can write it all down. All of what I'm going to say is true. I've done lots of detective work."

"OK, Cathy. I'm listening."

"My stepmother is going to meet the plane from Montreal at Kennedy Airport tomorrow, where she'll collect a packet of drugs from the big boss. She'll leave here at about 10 o'clock, and should be back at 11.30. She'll visit Johnnie in his apartment first. Then she'll come up here. Johnnie will go straight to a house in Harlem, where he'll sell the stuff to the dealers. I want you to take all this information to the police, Kev. My only worry is, will they believe you?"

"My Aunt Bella – she's the aunt I'm living with – knows the Lieutenant at the Precinct. She'll arrange things. Don't worry, Cathy. Everything will be all right. I wish I could use your key and come and see you at once, just to tell you not to worry."

"No, for heaven's sake! Keep right away. Don't forget, Johnnie's downstairs, and he knows you."

"Gosh, Cathy! Aren't you frightened?"

"Sometimes. But, Kev – don't, please don't forget to tell the police about my brother. That's terribly important."

"I won't, Cathy."

"Will we meet afterwards, Kev?" Cathy asked a bit anxiously.

"What a silly question!" Kevin said. "Bye, Cathy! It was great to hear your voice. Don't worry!"

He sat down on the couch and thought for a long time. Then he picked up the receiver and called Debbie's number.

"Debbie, do you think Mr. Swift would give us a holiday tomorrow?"

"You've forgotten. We have a holiday anyway. The French party hasn't arrived yet because of a strike at Charles de Gaulle Airport. Remember?"

---

14 **to arrange sth** to make sth possible – 31 **strike** when people stop working because they aren't happy about sth

"Debbie, could you possibly help me tomorrow – meet me with your car in Washington Square at 9 o'clock?"

"Sure, Kev. What's it all about?"

"Cathy and her stepmother. We're going to tell the police."

"How can I help you?"

"Just drive me to a place where I can see what happens."

"Is that sensible, Kev?"

"I don't see why not. I'm not going to do anything. But I guess it could be dangerous. I never thought of that. Forget I asked you, Debbie!"

"No, Kev," she said quickly. "I'll be in Washington Square at 9 o'clock."

"But what about Earle, Debbie? What'll he say if it's going to be dangerous?"

"Don't worry. Earle and I, we each do what we like. It'll be all right, Kev. See you at 9 o'clock."

"OK. It's a hundred to one we'll just sit and wait. Bye!"

When Aunt Bella came home an hour later, he told her what had happened. She hesitated.

"I know you, Kevin. You tell the truth. But …"

"What I've told you is completely true, Aunt Bella."

His aunt thought for a moment. Then she said, "Of course I'll call my friend the Lieutenant and tell him he must see you."

Kevin laughed. "I sure hope he does!"

Aunt Bella called the Precinct and asked for the Lieutenant. "Herb? Is that you? It's Bella speaking … No, I'm not calling you about the Puerto Ricans again … It may well be something more serious."

A half-hour later, Kevin was sitting at a table in the Precinct talking to the Lieutenant. The room was large, and there were policemen everywhere writing reports, typing, shouting at one another, drinking coffee. It was just like a scene from a TV police

20 **to tell the truth** *opp of* to tell lies – 31 **report** written text saying exactly what happened and what people said

drama. Kevin told the Lieutenant everything he knew. The
Lieutenant listened silently while another policeman took notes.

"Will you be able to get into the apartment easily?" Kevin asked
anxiously.

"No problem!" the Lieutenant replied. "That'll be the first thing   5
we do after Mrs. O'Brien has left for the airport."

"That's the best bit of news you've given me!" Kevin said,
putting his hand into his pocket to see if Cathy's key was still
there. He felt guilty that he had not told the Lieutenant about the
key.   10

"We'll call the Charleston police at once," the Lieutenant said,
"and put Cathy's brother under police protection." He got up and
put his hand on Kevin's shoulder. "That was a very good report
you gave. Ever thought of becoming a policeman?"

"Sometimes, yes," Kevin replied.   15

Think about it ...

Debbie says that many of the people who live
in Harlem are very poor, and where there is
poverty, there is crime.
Think of three adjectives to describe Debbie's
attitude.
What do you think?

---

9 **to feel guilty** to feel unhappy because you think you've done sth wrong – 12 **under
police protection** a special program where sb the police keep sb safe

7 Things go wrong

Kevin woke early. He put on his strongest shoes and a leather jacket and sat down to breakfast with Aunt Bella.

"The Lieutenant asked me if I'd like to be a policeman," he said.

"Herb reads character well," his aunt said. "Maybe he read yours."

Kevin finished his coffee and got up.

"Keep well away, Kev," his aunt said. "Remember, they know who you are."

"I'll try, Aunt Bella," Kevin said, and set off for Washington Square. Debbie was already there, waiting in her car.

They had nearly reached Eleventh Avenue, when they heard the sound of police sirens. It was quite usual to hear sirens in New York, but this time there were not only police cars but also several ambulances. When they reached Eleventh Avenue, Debbie stopped the car on the other side of the street, opposite the apartment house. Farther up the Avenue, there were crowds in the street, and the police were stopping all traffic.

---

to go wrong things don't run as planned – 19 to read sb's character to guess what sb is like – 27 siren sound made by ambulances, police cars and fire engines

"Must be a bad accident," Debbie said.

They sat and waited. They had a perfect view of the entrance to the apartment house. At five after ten, Mrs. O'Brien left, carrying a large bag. A moment or two later, a man in a dark raincoat came out of a doorway and followed her up the street.

"It's started, Debbie!" Kevin said. "In a minute you'll see a plain clothes policeman enter the lobby. After that, I don't know what's going to happen. The Lieutenant didn't tell me."

They waited. They heard the sound of sirens, but no traffic came up the Avenue. There was a strange quiet. The street leading to Tenth Avenue was empty. It was getting hot, but at Debbie's suggestion, they kept the windows up.

"When the sun is shining on the glass," she said, "they won't be able to see us."

As the minutes passed, Kevin kept looking at his watch. At last he said, "Something's wrong. It's almost 10.45. A few women have come through the lobby doors. That's all. Nobody has gone into the building."

"What are you going to do? Call the Precinct?"

"No. I'm going in there myself – if you'll help me."

"Me? What can I do?"

"Something very important, Debbie. If you could go into the lobby and persuade the security guard to come out and have a look at your car …"

"But there's nothing wrong with my car."

"We could loosen the leads to the spark plugs."

"You think if he came out you'd have enough time to get in and past the turnstiles?"

"Sure!"

"And what happens if you meet Johnnie? He may have a gun."

---

6 **plain clothes policeman** policeman who is not wearing uniform – 26 **to loosen** to make sth not so tight – 26 **the leads to the spark plugs** parts of the car

"I've learned a bit of karate, Debbie! Anyway, I don't think he'd shoot, because of the noise. And I'm sure he'll stay in his apartment until Mrs. O'Brien returns."

"But how are you going to get out again?"

"Please call the police as soon as you can. Tell them I'm in the apartment with Cathy, and we can't get out until they come. Find out what's happened at the Precinct."

"OK, Kev. Anything you say, sir!"

Kevin lifted the hood of Debbie's car and loosened the leads. Then he waved to Debbie, crossed the road and stood close to the wall in the empty street. He was only a few feet from the glass doors. A few moments later, Debbie walked into the building. She was there longer than he had expected, but he could hear laughter and soon afterwards she crossed the road with the security guard.

Kevin was inside the lobby in a flash. The gate beside the desk had been left open, and he ran through it to the elevators. He pressed the button for the ninth floor, and in another minute he was fitting the key into the lock of apartment 908. He pushed open the door.

Two arms embraced him. "Kevin! I thought I said, 'Keep away from here.'"

"Cathy! Are you all right?"

They sat on the couch and he told her they would have to stay there until the police came. Something had happened – he did not know what – but he was sure the police would be there soon.

"Where's the telephone, Cathy?" he suddenly said.

"It's gone. I don't know if she was suspicious, but today she's taken it right away. Kev – what about my brother?"

"He's under police protection in Charleston. Cathy, that day we met in Niagara Falls, did you see the man your stepmother was visiting in Montreal?"

---

16 **in a flash** very quickly – 21 **to embrace sb** to put your arms round sb

"No. She stopped on a lonely road and waited until another car arrived. She got into the other car and left me behind with a man to guard me. He didn't say a single word to me until my stepmother got back."

"Then you drove back to New York?"

"No. It was a rented car, you see. We left it at the car rental place in Montreal and went back to New York by train."

The time passed quickly. It was 11.45 by the clock on the wall. Suddenly they heard a noise in the passage outside and a key turned in the lock. Before they had time to get up, the door opened and Johnnie stood in front of them. They stared at one another, astonished.

"What the hell are you doin' here?" Johnnie said to Kevin.

"Visiting Cathy," Kevin said as coolly as possible.

"How the hell did you get in? This door doesn't open from inside without a special key, and she doesn't have one of those."

"What do you want, Johnnie?" Cathy said,

"Now that's real polite, I must say. A real nice welcome. Why don't you ask me if I'd like to sit down, and would I like a drink? OK, I'll tell you what I want. Your stepmother's in my apartment downstairs, and she doesn't feel too good."

"What's wrong with her?"

"Well, I guess she's kind of dead."

"You're a murderer!" Kevin shouted.

"Yes, kid – and she ain't the first – or the last!" He turned and stared at Cathy. "You know where she keeps her dough, Cathy? Show me where it is."

Cathy shook her head and Johnnie moved towards her.

"I don't know, Johnnie!" Cathy cried. "Honestly, I don't know!"

"Well, you'll come and help me find it, now, won't you?"

---

6 **rented car** a car you pay to use for a short time – 6 **car rental place** place where you can rent a car – 9 **passage** a small corridor or path – 12 **astonished** very surprised – 26 **dough** (slang) money

He took her by the arm. At the same time, Kevin kicked him as hard as possible on the leg. Johnnie roared with pain, dropped Cathy's arm and turned to Kevin. Kevin waited for him, his arms hanging loosely by his sides. Johnnie pulled a knife from his belt, but still Kevin did not move. As Johnnie suddenly rushed at him, Kevin caught his arm, turned him round and hit him with the side of the hand on the back of his neck. Johnnie crashed to the floor, the knife flying from his hand. He lay where he fell, without moving. Kevin went quickly down on his knees and listened to Johnnie's heart.

"He's not dead."

Cathy looked at Kevin with surprise and admiration.

"Gosh!" he said. "I didn't know I'd learnt karate so well!"

"There's someone else in the passage!" Cathy said.

Suddenly the door opened and two men with guns rushed in. One of them pointed at Johnnie on the floor.

---

7 **to crash to the floor** to fall to the floor heavily – 29 **admiration** respect

"That's the man we want!" he said. He turned to Kevin. "Did you do this?"

"Yes. He was attacking the girl."

"How did you do it? He's a dangerous guy."

"Karate! I learned it at high school, but of course he didn't know that. If he had known, I guess there'd have been a different ending! He told us he'd just killed Mrs. O'Brien, in his apartment."

"Yeah, we know. We're policemen."

"We were expecting you much earlier," Kevin said. "What happened?"

"An accident. Someone driving a stolen car ran into the Lieutenant's car and another police car. People on the sidewalk were hit, too. It was like a battlefield. Two policemen and three passers-by were taken to the hospital. The driver of the stolen car was killed."

Think about it ...

Kevin thinks that his basic knowledge of karate will help him if he finds that Johnnie has a gun. Do you agree?

In countries like the US a lot of people have guns. Why do you think they have them?
Do you think that gun laws should be changed to make it impossible to carry or use a gun?

14 **battlefield** place where a fight has taken place – 15 **passer-by** sb who walks past

8 Cathy comes to stay

"Come in, Cathy," Aunt Bella said. "I expect Kevin has told you that I shall be very pleased to have you come and stay here. You'll want to get a job, I imagine?"

Cathy took off her coat and sat on a chair. Kevin and Aunt Bella sat opposite her on the couch.

"Oh, yes," Cathy said. "I couldn't possibly stay here if I didn't pay for my keep."

"I think I'll stay in New York," Kevin said.

"Why don't you become a policeman?" Cathy said, laughing.

"I'm thinking about it," he answered seriously.

"Oh, no, Kev! I didn't mean it! It's a dangerous job."

"I'm glad they caught those dealers," Kevin said. "They didn't know what was happening on the West Side, so they were all in the house in Harlem, waiting for Johnnie."

"I hear your stepmother is getting better," Aunt Bella said.

"Yes. Johnnie really thought he had killed her, you know."

---

22 **to pay for your keep** to pay for the cost of your food etc

"He was too greedy," Kevin said. "He wanted her money as well as all the heroin she had brought back from the airport. It's a good thing they caught the man from Montreal as well."

"You were lucky to escape from Johnnie," Aunt Bella said. "I went to see Herb in the hospital, and he told me the guy had already killed two drug addicts because they had made trouble for the dealers."

"Did you say lucky?" Cathy cried. "You should have seen Kev! He just got hold of Johnnie's arm, and pulled him round, and then, bang! That was that! He was great!"

---

1 **greedy** wanting too much – 6 **drug addict** sb who can't stop taking drugs – 9 **to get/ take hold of sb/sth** to catch and hold sb/sth tightly

Activities

Focus on the story

Chapter 1: A meeting at Niagara Falls
Tick the correct sentences.

1 Kevin had finished school and was going to New York. ___
2 Kevin wanted to live in Niagara Falls with his aunt. ___
3 Betty was Kevin's girlfriend. ___
4 Cathy was very friendly with Kevin. ___
5 Cathy's parents died when she was young. ___
6 Kevin gave Cathy his address. ___
7 Cathy's step mother made Kevin suspicious. ___
8 Kevin left for New York with Cathy's key. ___

Chapter 2: Journey to New York
Read and choose the correct word(s).

1 Kevin crossed the border by using *a little ship / the bridge*.
2 He got to New York by *car / truck.*
3 Kevin bought *ten travel tickets / a travel card of ten dollars*.
4 The train station had a lot of *cars / commuters.*
5 The woman Kevin saw from behind *was / wasn't* Cathy.
6 The coffee shop where he had breakfast gave him *extra coffee / an extra breakfast* for free.
7 Aunt Bella spent a lot of money on *her hair / helping ethnic groups*.
8 Cathy's *boarding school / neighborhood* is dangerous.

Chapter 3: The search for Cathy begins
Correct the sentences.

1 Mrs O'Brien tried to stop Kevin from walking into her home.
2 Cathy's apartment building was empty with broken doors and windows.
3 Kevin was surprised to see a security guard in the apartment block.
4 Kevin knew he would recognise the man in the lobby again because he was African-American.
5 Kevin visited the Radio City Music Hall that day.
6 Kevin stopped at a snack bar to see a hot dog.
7 Kevin threw himself on the couch because he saw Aunt Bella.
8 Aunt Bella knows people who belong to gangs, are muggers and who kill people.

Chapter 4: Kevin tries again
Match the two halves of the sentences.

1 Kevin was sure
2 Aunt Bella gave him the precinct's number
3 The person in the Oldsmobile
4 The woman who helped Kevin knew
5 Kevin wanted to get off the bus so that the bald man
6 In the park Kevin
7 Kevin didn't return back home immediately because
8 Kevin can't go back to Cathy's apartment because

a she would be killed if she gave evidence.
b hid behind two people sitting in the grass.
c nothing would happen to him.
d he didn't want the black man to find out where he lived.
e wouldn't stop following him.
f in case Kevin needed help.
g he is starting work.
h wanted to kill Kevin.

1	2	3	4	5	6	7	8
c							

Chapter 5: The guide

Complete the sentences.

1 Mr Swift played different parts of _____ to see how Kevin would react.
2 Debbie and Kevin became _____.
3 Kevin decided to go back to the apartment after _____.
4 Kevin saw the bald man shouting at a rich _____.
5 Aunt Bella was sure that Cathy's mum was involved in a _____.
6 In the bank Kevin was surprised because he saw Cathy's stepmother with _____.
7 Kevin sees the bald man in a _____ talking to the rich teenager.
8 Kevin decides _____ Johnnie, the black man.

Chapter 6: A trip to Harlem

Tick the things that happen in this chapter.

Kevin ...
1. went into Madison Square Garden.
2. followed Johnnie into Harlem.
3. went into the house in 127th Street.
4. called Cathy.

Cathy ...

5. explained why she couldn't talk to or see Kevin.
6. gave Kevin important information about the next drug deal.
7. told Kevin to tell the police that her brother was in danger.

Kevin...
8. goes to Charles de Gaulle.
9. watched a police TV drama.

Chapter 7: Things go wrong

Read and answer T for True and F for False.

1. The Lieutenant thinks Kevin would be a good policeman. ___
2. The police would wear normal clothes and go into Cathy's apartment. ___
3. Debbie's car breaks down. ___
4. Kevin and Cathy waited for Mrs O'Brien. ___
5. Cathy's brother is safe. ___
6. Johnnie wants to sit down and have a drink. ___
7. Kevin hurt Johnnie by doing karate. ___
8. The police were late because they had an accident. ___

Chapter 8: Cathy comes to stay

Answer the questions.

1 Why does Cathy want to get a job?
2 What is Kevin thinking about?
3 How were the dealers caught?
4 Is Cathy's stepmother dead?
5 Why was Johnnie greedy?
6 Who had killed two drug addicts?

The best scene is ....

What was your favorite scene in each chapter?

Chapter:	My favorite scene is …	because….
1		
2		
3		
4		
5		
6		
7		
8		

Focus on grammar

1 Which preposition fits best?
Complete these phrases with the right preposition.

of (x2)	about	at	in	to	for	with

1 afraid ___ a ghost
2 surprised ___ his behaviour
3 difficulty ___ understanding you
4 threaten ___ kill me
5 look ___ my phone
6 talk ___ the accident
7 full ___ people
8 thinking ___ you

2 Adjective of adverb?
Underline the word which sounds best in each sentence.

1 Joe spoke to me quite *angry / angrily*.
2 Helen looked at the list *carefully / careful*.
3 We waited *anxious / anxiously* for the doctor to tell us the news.
4 George is a very *serious / seriously* young boy.
5 Wendy is a *cheerfully / cheerful* person.
6 The tour guide was very *friendly / friend*.

Build your vocabulary

Focus on words and phrases

1 Match the US English words to the British English words.

apartment	taxi
elevator	lorry
trash	flat
cab	sofa
check	lift
freeway	bill
hood	rubbish
truck	bonnet
subway	motorway
couch	underground

2 Make sentences with the words from activity 1. You only need 6 words. Use US or UK words.

1 We used the _____ to get to the 34th floor of the building.
2 Our car broke down in the middle of the _____ on our way to the countryside.
3 Barry felt bad when he didn't have enough money to pay for the restaurant _____.
4 It's important to always take our _____ with us instead of leaving it in open spaces.
5 Jenny lives in a small _____ in upstate Manhattan but it has a beautiful view of the park.
6 We often take the _____ downtown because it is quicker than the bus.

3 Choose the best definition of each of these expressions from the story:

> 1 without a moment's hesitation

a do something very quickly
b do something without thinking about it anymore
c do something in a minute

> 2 get into your thick head

a too dumb to understand
b put on your mind
c finally understand something after being told many times

3 get rid of him

a make sure he goes away and never comes back
b put him in the bin
c make sure he gets lost

4 your father's son

a your brother
b a son who the same personality as his father.
c your stepbrother

5 sign a death warrant

a a certificate showing a death
b a paper showing you will die
c an agreement to allow someone to kill you

6 I'm a bad sailor

a a person who gets sea sick
b a sailor who doesn't do his job well
c a pirate

7 comings and goings

a to come and go somewhere
b what is happening in a place
c the problems of a place

8 like a battlefield

a   a place where people fight
b   a place where there was a war
c   a game

4 Law and order

There are a lot of words about law and order in this story.
Can you complete the crossword?

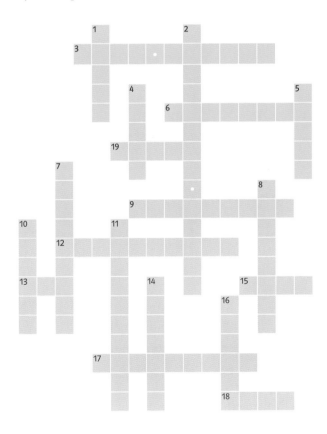

Across

3 an official document which gives somebody permission to work in a foreign country

6 another word for police station

9 an adjective that describes a person, animal or situation that could harm you

12 another word for chief police officer

13 a weapon to shoot with

15 illegal substance taken for pleasure, to improve someone's ability to perform, or because they cannot stop using it

17 a member of a police force

18 to cause somebody to die

19 building where trials or other legal processes take place; gathering of people (officials) that decide whether someone is guilty

Down

1 slang expression for money

2 person whose job it is to prevent people from going into places without permission

4 slang expression for a very dishonest person, especially a criminal

5 to take something without the permission or knowledge of the owner

7 a car used to take sick or injured people to hospital

8 somebody who illegally and intentionally kills another person

10 somebody who attacks people and steals their money

11 an adjective describing a person that is acting in a strange, mysterious and perhaps illegal way

14 the act of attacking someone and stealing their money

16 to try to hurt or defeat somebody using violence

5. Escape in New York – the mindmap

Make your own mindmap words connected to the story. Think of words to add to each topic area. You can add your own topic areas too. (**Design as a mindmap – words in main bubbles in normal font, examples in "handwriting". At least one page**).

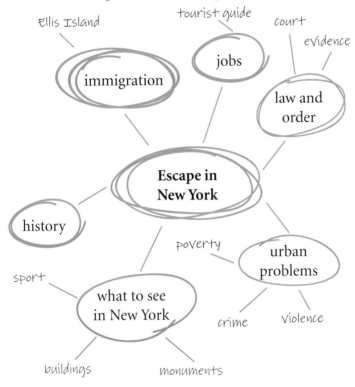

Compare your words with the words in on the next pages. Did you include some of the same words? Tick the words you know and look back at the text and explanations to check the meanings of any new words. You can add your own words and notes to the glossary like the examples here.

Glossary

	New word?	Notes / connected words
Immigration		
cross the border	☐	
ethnic groups	☐	
hard time	☐	
passport	☐	
work permit	☐	
History		
Ellis Island	☐	
monument	☐	
Revolutionary War	☐	
Jobs		
businessman	☐	
driver	☐	
police officer	☐	
secretary	☐	
security guard	☐	
tourist guide	☐	
Law and order		
be in serious trouble	☐	
cops	☐	
court	☐	
evidence	☐	
robbers	☐	
under police protection	☐	